Should I Take My Dog to the Vet?

A Pet Owner's Guide to Signs of Illness

Renee D. Fisher DVM

SHOULD I TAKE MY DOG TO THE VET?

A Pet Owner's Guide To Signs Of Illness

RENEE D FISHER, DVM

Contents

This book is dedicated to all of my loyal and dedicated clients and their pets. You have taught me to strive for continual improvement in honing my veterinary skills and have deepened my own understanding and the true meaning of the human/animal bond. Thank you all!

Introduction/Disclaimer

Two of the most common questions clients ask when phoning our veterinary hospital are: "Do I have to bring my dog in?" and "Is there anything I can try at home first?" Realistically, the veterinary receptionists, the veterinary technicians, and even the veterinarians themselves, cannot accurately make a diagnosis and recommend an appropriate treatment regimen over the phone.

An accurate assessment and response to your questions require, at minimum, a complete and thorough physical examination. Pictures and videos can be helpful as an aid to be used in conjunction with the physical examination; however, an accurate assessment can seldom be derived when used alone. Depending on the physical examination findings, other diagnostic tests may be recommended to make a definitive diagnosis. These tests may include bloodwork, a urinalysis, other lab work, radiographs (x-rays), ultrasound, CT scans, MRIs, etc. These tests may result in a diagnosis or they may show the need for further testing to pursue an accurate diagnosis in order to develop an appropriate treatment plan.

Our pets cannot tell us what is wrong or how they feel or what hurts. What the owner sees is largely subjective and may be completely different than what the veterinarian actually finds on examination.

Two cases in particular come to mind:

1. A cat was brought in for a urinary issue because he was peeing in the back burner of the stove. His urine always tested normal. Instead, we diagnosed a severe skin problem caused by an allergy. We treated his skin and he stopped. However, every time his skin/allergy flared up, he peed in the back burner of the stove.

2. A well-meaning pet owner checked with Dr. Google. Their miniature poodle was brought in for "bloat," which is a severe and life-threatening

condition, primarily of large-breed dogs, where the stomach fills with gas, which cannot be expelled, and commonly results in a twisting of the stomach, cutting off the blood supply. The dog actually had lumbar disc disease. He had hurt his back and was standing all hunched up because of back pain.

This book is neither meant to be complete nor is it intended to replace your veterinarian. This book is meant only to mention some of the more common clinical signs of health problems your pet may manifest and point out that in almost all cases, "Yes, you should take your dog to the vet!"

The lists of clinical signs, possible diagnoses, and suggestions for home remedies are also not meant to be exhaustive. Indeed, many different medical conditions, some benign and some very serious, may be manifested by your pet in the very same way. Sometimes your dogs forget to read the book and the accurate diagnosis may be masked by a completely different set of symptoms. The body only has so many ways to show signs of disease. Your veterinarian is the only one qualified to make these distinctions.

This book is also not intended to be a complete and exhaustive veterinary reference journal or a medical textbook. It is only meant as a guide for the layperson to understand some of the more common disease syndromes that may underlie the symptoms shown by your pet and why, in most cases, "Yes, you should take your dog to the vet!"

2

Skin And Ears

Yes, You Should Take Your Dog To The Vet!

. . .

Next to routine vaccination and wellness examinations, skin and ear problems make up the number one presenting complaint I have from my dog-owning clients. Diagnosing the underlying cause of itchiness, sores, and hair loss can be very complicated. Your veterinarian may have to perform a multitude of tests to make an accurate diagnosis and, because skin and ear problems may be associated with other chronic conditions, may require you to make multiple appointments to re-check your dog's progress in order to keep the problems under control.

What It Could Be:

1. Parasite
2. Reaction To A Drug Or Insect Bite/Sting
3. Reaction To An Irritant In The Environment
4. Allergy
5. Infection/Pyoderma
6. Hormonal Imbalance/Endocrine Disorder
7. Immune-mediated Disease
8. Cancer
9. Other - Anything Not Mentioned

Parasite

Many different types of parasites can wreak havoc on your pet's skin and ears. In addition to the common parasites such as fleas, ticks, and ear mites, your dog may also become infested with mange mites like scabies or the Demodex mite, Cheyletiella, maggots, or lice. Infestation may present as itching, open sores, rashes, and/or hair loss. As secondary bacterial and/or fungal infections set in, your pet may develop an odor or have pus exude from the ears or the skin lesions. Your veterinarian will usually identify the parasite by seeing it on your pet's skin, hair, or in the ears during the examination, or by gathering skin scrapings, hair combings, or ear swabs to examine under the microscope. Mites that live in the ears or under the surface of the skin cannot be seen with the naked eye.

Reaction To A Drug Or Insect Bite/Sting

On occasion, your pet may have an allergic reaction to a drug administered by your veterinarian. Far more commonly, these reactions occur from some over-the-counter (OTC) medication purchased at a local store or from an insect bite or sting. These reactions vary in severity. Sometimes only mild itching and redness may occur. However, many times, the entire face and ears will swell up, and your pet may experience welts or hives.

In severe cases, a systemic reaction will occur and your pet will have difficulty breathing. In any of these instances you should seek veterinary care immediately. Benadryl can be given at home; however, since the dosage is based on your pet's weight, you should call your veterinarian to make sure you are giving the proper amount.

Please also note that many small dogs and cats experience neurologic symptoms, such as tremors, twitching, and seizures from using OTC flea and tick products, which may be more toxic to the pet than to the flea or tick.

Irritant/Allergy

There are certain chemicals and other materials that will cause your pet to itch just by coming into contact with them. These materials include certain types of straws, grasses, mulches, blankets, carpeting, or other bedding (especially if moldy), etc. along with chemicals like Clorox or other acids or alkalinizing solutions. These materials are known as contact irritants.

Some pets have food allergies. These allergies usually manifest as itching, before the puppy is even a year old, and are poorly responsive to medications used to treat allergies. Although some pets may be allergic to corn and grains, the majority of food allergies are caused by the protein source in the diet. Contrary to popular belief, your pet does not need the new fad "gluten-free" or "corn-free" diet.

Stick with a name-brand dog food in which clinical trials have been run to make sure that the diet is nutritionally complete. Examples of name-brand diets include (but are not limited to) Purina, Science Diet, Royal Canin, and Blue Buffalo. If your pet has a food allergy and is itchy, or having digestive issues, a food elimination diet must be performed to identify, then eliminate, the offending protein. Your pet may then need to eat only a prescription diet—specifically formulated for a dog with a food allergy—that is also nutritionally complete.

By far, the most common form of allergies are flea allergies (allergy to the saliva in a flea bite) and atopy (inhaled allergens). These allergies manifest as itching, after the puppy is one year of age, and include exposure to fleas, pollens, dusts, molds, weeds, grasses, trees—the list is endless.

Many dogs are allergic to house dust, and house dust mites, which are present in the normal materials found in your home such as carpeting, mattresses, furniture, and curtains. Think of how allergies manifest in people: where people cough, sneeze, and wheeze, dogs itch and scratch and get ear infections. In people, ears, nose, and throat (ENT) go together. In dogs, ears and skin go together, both treated in the dermatology department. Both people and dogs can break out in hives or welts depending on the type of allergy.

Dogs with flea allergies will scratch, lick, bite, and chew their rear ends, bellies, and rear legs/inner thighs. A dog with a flea allergy only needs to be bitten by one flea and he/she may itch for two to three weeks from that one flea bite. Dogs with atopy lick and chew their feet and rub their faces and ears. They may be itchy all over. If nothing is done to relieve the itching, many dogs will scratch, bite, and chew themselves raw, resulting in open sores in addition to hair loss. Many people who have dogs with allergies think they have mange because of the sores and hair loss caused by the severe itching and scratching.

The very best way to diagnose allergies and administer proper treatment is to visit your veterinarian. Depending on his/her level of dermatological experience and expertise, allergy testing may be recommended. The most accurate test is the intradermal skin test. There are also serologic tests available that are not as specific. In addition, immune therapists have come out with certain medications that work by modifying the immune system and preventing the allergic reaction despite the actual cause of the allergy. These new immune therapies seem to be very effective.

Infection/Pyoderma

Skin infections or pyodermas may be primary—resulting from an injury or a weakened immune response to bacteria or fungi—or they could be secondary to other conditions such as allergies, hypothyroidism, immune-mediated disease, or cancer. In some instances, the pet's immune system cannot control the numbers of the normal bacteria (usually a Staph species) on their skin. Some pets are actually allergic to the normal Staph bacteria that live on their skin. Self-trauma resulting from excessive scratching, biting, licking, and chewing, secondary to parasites and other allergies, will often cause skin infections. Some of these infections may be superficial and mild. Others are very deep and serious. Dogs can also get yeast infections caused by Malassezia spp. or fungal infections such as ringworm.

Both bacteria and yeast can cause ear infections in dogs. Ear infections may have severe consequences if left untreated or if not treated appropriately. Most dogs present with an otitis externa or infection of the ear canals and outer ear. Without proper treatment, the eardrum may rupture, allowing the infection to enter the middle ear (otitis media) and the inner ear (otitis interna). When this happens, neurologic changes may take place affecting your dog's hearing and balance.

The constant head shaking and scratching of the ears may result in a hematoma where the cartilage layers of the ear pinnae (ear flaps) separate and fill with blood. An ear hematoma needs to be surgically corrected to prevent severe scarring and disfigurement as with a "cauliflower ear." In addition, chronic ear infections will result in thickening and calcification of the ear canals. The cartilage in the ear canal literally turns to bone.

The ear canal is often swollen shut, preventing medication from getting in and pus from getting out.

These dogs are in severe pain and need surgical procedures such as a lateral ear canal resection or a total ear canal ablation to get rid of the infection and damaged tissue and to relieve pain.

Dogs with chronic skin and ear infections need to have skin scrapings and ear swabs performed to rule out mites. Bacterial and/or fungal culture and sensitivities need to be performed to identify what type of infection is present and what drug will work best to treat it. Blood tests may need to be performed to rule out hypothyroidism or Cushing's disease. My preference is to have a complete thyroid panel run at Michigan State University because they test for Free T4 (FT4 the active form of thyroid hormone in the dog), thyroid stimulating hormone, and T3 and T4 autoantibodies. The in-house Total T4 (TT4) test run in most veterinary hospitals is not accurate for diagnosis of hypothyroidism in dogs. Once treatment is started, repeat Free T4 blood tests may need to be performed to monitor therapeutic levels of the supplemented thyroid hormone.

Hormonal Imbalances

As mentioned above, endocrine or hormonal imbalances may be the underlying cause of many chronic skin and ear infections. In addition to skin and ear disease, hypothyroidism may cause increased appetite, weight gain, lethargy, hair loss, lichenification (thickening of the skin, leathery skin), and hyperpigmentation (black discoloration of the skin). After diagnosis, thyroid replacement therapy and monitoring need to be instituted.

Tumors or cysts on the ovaries and Sertoli cell tumors of the testicles will often result in hair loss due to excessive estrogen secretion. Clinical signs may be similar to hypothyroidism. Surgery is required to correct these disorders, and they can only be diagnosed by a thorough physical examination and appropriate lab work.

Tumors of the adrenal glands or pituitary gland may cause Cushing's disease where excessive cortisol production results in increased appetite, weight gain, hair loss, thin skin, and a pot-bellied appearance. Please also note that iatrogenic Cushing's disease may be caused by chronic overuse of steroids like prednisone, dexamethasone, betamethasone, triamcinolone, and many others.

Steroids have some wonderful therapeutic proper-ties, but should be used at their lowest effective dose and as infrequently as possible in order to avoid iatrogenic Cushing's disease.

All of these hormonal imbalances are diagnosed and monitored with a variety of blood tests. Surgical intervention is used where appropriate.

Immune-Mediated Disease

Dogs may develop immune-mediated disorders in which the host immune system actually attacks its own skin cells causing irritation, infection, open sores, and itching. These diseases include the Bullous Pemphigoid disorders and Lupus. Immune-mediated disorders are diagnosed by examination, skin biopsies, and histopathology. Then appropriate immunotherapy is instituted. Only your veterinarian can identify these disorders.

Cancer

Lumps, bumps, and open sores that don't heal need to be checked by your veterinarian. A fine needle aspirate with cytology may be used to help decide if a lump needs to be surgically removed. If indicated, the lesion will be surgically removed and/or biopsied and histopathology will reveal if cancer is present and if the lesion is benign or malignant.

Things You Might Try At Home:

1. Make sure your pet is on an effective and safe flea- and tick-preventative medication. Some of these preparations will also treat certain mites and lice. The flea and tick medication you use on your pet should be recommended by your veterinarian! Remember that many of the OTC (over the counter) flea and tick products are not effective against fleas or ticks and may even cause severe toxic reactions, especially in small dogs and cats.
2. Make sure your pet is on a proper diet that is nutritionally complete.
3. Cool/tepid water baths with an oatmeal-based shampoo may help to soothe itching.
4. OTC antihistamine. Please check with your veterinarian on the specific drug and dosage.

In conclusion, the best thing to do if your dog has a skin or ear issue is to make an appointment with your veterinarian. A complete dermatology work-up may or may not be warranted, but may include skin scrapings, ear swabs, bacterial and fungal cultures and sensitivities, food elimination diets, serum testing or intradermal skin testing for allergies, blood testing for hormonal disorders, and skin biopsies. Treatment often involves a combination of diet and medications such as antibiotics, steroids, antihistamines, immunotherapy, hormonal supplements, medicated shampoos, and sometimes surgery. So, truthfully, if your pet has a skin or ear problem, "Yes, you should take your dog to the vet!"

Vomiting And Diarrhea

What It Could Be:

1. Intestinal Parasites - "Worms," Coccidia, etc.
2. Viruses/Bacteria - "GI Bug"
3. Dietary Indiscretion/GI Foreign Body/Gastroenteritis/Colitis
4. Hemorrhagic Gastroenteritis (HGE)
5. Gastric Dilatation/Volvulus Syndrome - "Bloat"
6. Pancreatitis
7. Systemic/Metabolic/Endocrine Disorders
8. Other/Idiopathic - "They Got It But We Don't Know Why They Got It"

Intestinal Parasites

Intestinal parasites include worms that you can see, such as roundworm and tapeworm; worms which are not usually seen because of their small size, such as hookworm and whipworm; and protozoal parasites that cannot be seen because they are microscopic, such as Giardia, Eimeria, Isospora, Toxoplasma, and other coccidia. The eggs of these parasites are shed in the bowel movement of animals that harbor them, then these eggs are picked up through ingestion of grass, etc.

from a contaminated environment, or from hunting, or passed from mother to offspring during whelping and nursing.

Most puppies and kittens are born with roundworm and/or hookworm infestations they acquire from the mother either in the womb or shortly after birth through nursing. The mother can then reinfest herself when she licks the puppies to stimulate bowel movements and clean them. Because of the life cycles of the worms, the infective larvae, which are ingested by the mother through eating grass, picking up sticks, licking the ground, (yes) eating poop, or hunting and eating small animals, may lie dormant in the mother's other body tissues for months or years until they migrate to the intestinal tract, the uterus, and the mammary glands during pregnancy. This can happen even if the mother's stool sample tested negative prior to whelping.

Contrary to popular belief, many of these parasites are not seen by the owner due to their small size, despite the owner's vigilance in visually checking their pet's stool. Most infestations are detected by identifying the eggs of the parasite on a routine fecal examination by your veterinarian during an annual physical examination or a sick patient visit.

Because the eggs of these parasites look different and because the medications used to treat them may be vastly different, your veterinarian is the only one qualified to identify the specific type of parasite your pet harbors in order to prescribe the appropriate medication. This is an important point because, not only can puppies and adult dogs die from these infestations if not properly treated, many of them are zoonotic, meaning they can spread to humans as well.

Because of this zoonotic potential, all puppies and kittens should be dewormed when they are three weeks old and five weeks old, then every two weeks as appropriate. All adult dogs should have a routine fecal examination performed on their stool at least annually during their well patient visit. Many of the newer heartworm and flea and tick preventatives also contain medications that treat some of these parasitic infestations.

Viruses And Bacteria - The "GI Bug"

Dogs may experience vomiting and diarrhea, with or without a fever, with no apparent cause. They can acquire a variety of viral and bacterial infections that manifest with gastrointestinal (GI) signs, just as people can. These infections may be mild and self-limiting or they may be severe and cause death. For example, unvaccinated puppies and adult dogs who are infected with Parvovirus will present with severe vomiting, dehydration, and bloody diarrhea. They require lab work, hospitalization, injectable medications, and aggressive fluid therapy to survive. Most of these patients will die without medical treatment. The longer the owner waits, the poorer the prognosis for survival. Please keep in mind that vomiting dogs cannot hold down food and/or water, so they will also vomit any oral medications given. They usually need to be hospitalized so they can be treated with injectable medications and intravenous (IV) fluids until they can hold down food and water.

Dietary Indiscretion/Foreign Bodies

Dietary indiscretion happens when your pet eats something he or she normally doesn't or shouldn't eat. Puppies are notorious for chewing up and eating things they shouldn't; anything from socks and underwear to carpeting, balls, rocks, toys, knives... the list is endless. If it can be swallowed, it is fair game. Sometimes these objects pass through the stomach and intestines with minimal problems. Other times, they get lodged along the way and cannot pass. If an object becomes lodged in the stomach or intestine and cannot pass, the pet will exhibit persistent vomiting, especially if he/she tries to eat. These dogs are hungry, but they vomit anything they attempt to eat or drink.

In this situation, radiographs and lab work may be necessary to diagnose the obstruction, but ultimately, the only treatment is to have the object surgically removed. The longer it remains in the digestive tract, the more sick and dehydrated your pet will become and the more likely permanent damage to those organs will occur, which then may require portions of the stomach and intestines to be removed as well.

Gastroenteritis And Colitis

Gastroenteritis is an inflammation of the stomach and small intestine in which vomiting may be noticed shortly after eating. Colitis is an inflammation of the colon, or large intestine, in which bloody or mucousy diarrhea is observed. These conditions can be caused by parasites, viruses, or bacteria. They may also be caused by dietary indiscretion or inflammatory conditions such as Inflammatory Bowel Disease (IBD).

There is a type of colitis called a "stress induced colitis" that results after a pet is kenneled, or at holiday time when you have company for the holidays in a normally peaceful household. In this case, the colitis is caused by something different in your dog's daily routine. Colitis may also be caused if your pet is fed table food or gets into the garbage. Although there is no obstruction, the pet ate something different than he/she normally eats, which causes irritation to the digestive tract. However, vomiting and diarrhea may be caused by something as simple as changing dog foods or giving your pet a new treat. In these cases, the clinical signs may not abate unless treated with appropriate medications by your veterinarian.

HGE - Hemorrhagic Gastroenteritis

In contrast to regular runny diarrhea or diarrhea with blood and mucous in it, HGE is characterized by profuse liquid diarrhea appearing as frank blood. Its cause is unknown but, HGE is a medical emergency. Your pet will become very sick very fast and will die within 24–48 hours if not hospitalized and given rapid intravenous fluid therapy, which only your veterinarian can provide.

Bloat

"Bloat" or Gastric Dilatation/Volvulus Syndrome is characterized by sudden abdominal distension resulting from gas buildup in the stomach. In the worst case scenario, the stomach twists on itself, preventing the escape of food, fluid, and gas. In the process, the blood flow to the stomach is severely compromised resulting in severe pain and shock. If not detected early, and corrected by a veterinary surgeon, these dogs will die an incredibly painful death. Even with surgery, the prognosis for survival is guarded depending on the damage to the stomach and the resulting shock and electrolyte imbalances, which then lead to cardiac complications. These pets may die even a couple of weeks after a successful surgery due to these cardiac complications.

Systemic/Metabolic/Endocrine Disorders

Many other disease syndromes can cause vomiting and diarrhea. Metabolic and electrolyte imbalances may cause nausea, gastric ulcers, megaesophagus, and other physical symptoms. These other disease syndromes include, but are not limited to: liver disease, kidney disease, diabetes mellitus, Addison's Disease, pancreatitis, neoplasia (cancer) and many others.

I would like to make a special note on pancreatitis. One of the causes of pancreatitis is owners feeding their dogs excessive fat, often in the form of "people food." Pancreatitis is characterized by lipemia (excessive fat in the blood). One thing you can do at home is to feed your pet a name brand dog food and not "people food" as dog food is more nutritionally complete, without excess fat, carbs, and salt.

None of the above diseases can be diagnosed and treated without your veterinarian.

Is There Anything I Can Try At Home First?

If diarrhea is the only symptom, food should be withheld from the pet for eight to twelve hours to let the digestive system "rest" (not in tiny/toy breed dogs and puppies). Your pet can have water. If there is no vomiting, a bland diet can be introduced after that time. You can offer the pet boiled chicken or boiled hamburger, mixed half and half with some boiled white rice (no skin or butter). For small dogs, all meat baby food such as chicken or turkey can be offered. Small, frequent meals should be fed every four to six hours until you see that the diarrhea is subsiding.

If vomiting is also present, both food and water should be withheld (not in tiny/toy breed dogs and puppies). After eight to twelve hours, offer water first, in small frequent amounts. You could also offer ice cubes made of water or homemade or low sodium chicken broth. When your pet can hold the water down, then add the bland diet in small frequent amounts.

Please note that young puppies and tiny/toy breed dogs cannot go for eight hours without eating or their blood sugar will drop too low, which can result in seizures. Sometimes puppies and toy breed dogs get nauseous and vomit in the morning due to an empty stomach because their owners take their food away too early in the evening so they will not have to go out to poop at night. In the case of a puppy or toy breed dog, a bland diet should be offered to the pet every two hours. You can also try small, frequent amounts of all-meat baby food such as turkey or chicken.

In Summary

If vomiting and diarrhea persist for a maximum of forty-eight hours, "Yes, you should take your dog to the vet!"

If you see signs of abdominal distention and discomfort, "Yes, you should take your dog to the vet!" This may be a medical emergency. If you see frank blood in the stool and lethargy, "Yes, you should take your dog to the vet!" This may be a medical emergency.

If you see worms, a stool sample should be evaluated by your veterinarian so that the proper worm medication can be prescribed and administered. If your pet has been dewormed and the vomiting and/or diarrhea persist, "Yes, you should take your dog to the vet!" This may or may not be a medical emergency but should be promptly addressed for the pet's sake and the possible consequences of dehydration for the pet and zoonotic infection to the owner.

If the vomiting subsides, but recurs every time your pet tries to eat, "Yes, you should take your dog to the vet!" The pet is hungry but can't eat. This is one of the classic signs of obstruction.

If the vomiting and/or diarrhea persist despite withholding food and water (vomiting on an empty stomach), "Yes, you should take your dog to the vet!"

Because persistent vomiting and diarrhea of more than forty-eight hours (less than that in a small puppy or toy breed dog) will result in weight loss, hypoglycemia (low blood sugar), dehydration, electrolyte imbalances, and eventually death. To be on the safe side, "Yes, you should take your dog to the vet!"

Drinking A Lot Of Water And Urinating Frequently/ Accidents In The House/ Bloody Urine

What It Could Be:

1. Urinary Tract Infection
2. Pyometra
3. Cystic Or Renal Calculi - Bladder Stones Or Kidney Stones
4. Cancer
5. Diabetes Mellitus - "Sugar" Diabetes
6. Diabetes Insipidus
7. Kidney Disease
8. Liver Disease
9. Cushing's Disease
10. Prostate Disease
11. Other - Anything Else Not Mentioned

Urinary Tract Infections

A urinary tract infection is diagnosed by running a urinalysis and possibly a urine culture and sensitivity. Once your veterinarian has evaluated your pet and the urine, appropriate antibiotics and other medications may be prescribed.

Pyometra

A pyometra occurs in an unspayed female dog, typically about four to six weeks after her last heat cycle. Because of hormonal changes influencing the endometrial lining and bacterial ascension from the lower urinary/vaginal tract, an infection of the uterus results. The uterus then fills with pus, causing an internal abdominal abscess. Open pyometras (the cervix opens to allow drainage) show a vaginal discharge of bloody or purulent material, often with the comment that, "Gee, Doc, she was just in heat and never came out" or "Gee, Doc, she was just in heat, went out, then came back in."

Closed pyometras (in which the cervix stays closed) result in no vaginal discharge. However, the dog will get much sicker, much faster, if the abscess is not allowed to drain. Early signs of pyometra include drinking excessive amounts of water and excessive urination, fever, lethargy, and inappetance. Pyometra is on the differential diagnosis list of any unspayed female dog not feeling well. The only treatment, once symptoms manifest, is to spay her, accompanied by supportive care. If not addressed surgically, the majority of these patients will die.

Cystic Or Renal Calculi

Calculi are stones that form in the urine, either in the kidney or in the urinary bladder itself. These stones are generally diagnosed through a urinalysis, abdominal radiographs and contrast studies, or abdominal ultrasound. Treatment involves either surgical removal or dietary management, depending on the type of stone. Frequent urine rechecks are often required as the most common type of bladder stone is struvite (a calculus made of magnesium, calcium, and phosphorus), which forms in association with long-term, low-grade urinary tract infections.

Other types of calculi may also form in association with other disease syndromes. For example, dalmations and dogs with certain liver conditions may form uric acid calculi. Because there is a bone in the male dog penis, these diseases are often diagnosed because the stone acts as a ball valve and causes an obstruction in the urethra, which prevents the pet from being able to urinate. Less frequently, any type of stone may cause a urethral obstruction in female dogs as well. These are examples of emergency situations as the backup of urine will cause severe kidney damage and even death if not diagnosed and surgically treated immediately. Many times your veterinarian will recommend a prescription diet to minimize or prevent recurrence of these stones

Prostate Disease

In most cases, prostate disease is caused by testosterone secretion in unneutered male dogs. The most common manifestations of prostate disease are: fever, blood in the urine, frequent urination, or pain/straining to urinate or defecate. Flattened ribbon-like feces may also be noted with severe enlargement. Depending on the syndrome, conditions such as benign prostatic hyperplasia, prostatic cysts, prostatic abscesses, and prostatitis are often treated by a combination of castration and antibiotics or other medications. Neutering your male dog at a young age significantly reduces the risk of developing prostate disease later in life. The prognosis for a dog with malignant prostate cancer is very poor.

All Disease Syndromes On This List

All of the above conditions require veterinary attention for diagnosis and treatment. Often, bloodwork, labwork, radiographs, and sometimes surgery are required to treat your pet. If your pet exhibits any of the signs above, such as drinking a lot of water, urinating frequently, blood in the urine or straining to urinate or defecate, "Yes, you should take your dog to the vet!"

Unexplained Weight Loss

What It Could Be:

1) Worms Or Other Parasites

2) Chronic Disease

3) Malnutrition/Malabsorption/Maldigestion

4) Systemic/Metabolic/Endocrine Disorders

5) Infection

6) Cancer

7) Idiopathic/Other- Anything Not Mentioned

"Yes, you should take your dog to the vet!" All of these serious conditions require veterinary attention, including certain types of lab work and/or special diagnostics for proper diagnosis and appropriate treatment.

Worms Or Other Parasites

Worms or other parasites have been previously discussed and deserve another mention. They require a thorough physical examination in order to determine what type of test needs to be run to diagnose the issue. Fecal (stool) sample exams are used for GI parasites. They are also used to diagnose lung worms and worms that live in the kidneys and other tissues and organs. Some kidney worms shed their eggs in the urine. Blood tests are run for blood parasites. Radiographs may need to be taken or ultrasound employed to identify obstructions or organ enlargement or other abnormalities.

Chronic Disease

Any long-standing medical condition including, but not limited to: heart disease, liver disease, kidney disease, cancer, etc. may present as unexplained weight loss.

Malnutrition/Malabsorption/Maldigestion

Malnutrition occurs when the pet is not fed enough or not fed a proper diet. Malabsorption occurs when the pet eats well but continues to lose weight with no other apparent cause. Even though the pet is eating, its digestive system cannot absorb the nutrients. Maldigestion occurs because the food that the pet is eating cannot be digested properly. One example of maldigestion is exocrine pancreatic insufficiency where the pancreas does not produce the enzymes necessary for digestion of food. If the food is not digested properly, it cannot be absorbed properly. Special diagnostic tests are required for diagnosis and appropriate treatment of all of the above disorders, which may or may not be related.

Systemic/Metabolic/Endocrine Disorders

These disorders include, but are not limited to: heart disease, liver disease, kidney disease, diabetes mellitus, exocrine pancreatic insufficiency, etc. Once again, special diagnostic tests are required for accurate diagnosis and appropriate treatment.

Infection

Many infections are caused by—or produce—a suppression of the immune system, which weakens the body. Often, infections cause fevers, which result in inappetence. Without the appropriate antimicrobial, as determined by the type of infection and which body systems are affected, many of these infections will not resolve spontaneously. Many times a culture will be performed to identify the offending organism if caused by bacteria or fungi. Then a sensitivity test will be performed to identify which antimicrobials are effective against this particular bacterium or fungus. Sometimes serology must be run to identify the offending organism, especially if viral.

Cancer

Most types of malignant cancers will result in weight loss if left untreated. Metastasis (spread) of the malignancy can affect many organs of the body depending on the type of cancer, which can only be determined by your veterinarian through examination and diagnostic testing.

Idiopathic/Other

There are many other causes for unexplained weight loss. Sometimes the diagnosis is not made until after the pet's death by performing a necropsy and examining and biopsying various tissue samples.

As you can see, the list of possibilities is extensive. So, in all cases of unexplained weight loss, "Yes, you should take your dog to the vet!"

6

Coughing, Sneezing, Wheezing, Difficult Or Labored Breathing

What It Could Be:

1) Bacterial, Viral, Or Fungal Infection

2) Inflammatory/Asthma/Allergy

3) Heart Or Lung Disease

4) Parasites - Heartworm Disease

5) Cancer

6) Anemia

7) Other - Anything Not Mentioned

Bacterial, Viral, Or Fungal Infections

Many types of bacteria, viruses, and fungi can be responsible for airway disease. Upper respiratory disease involves infection of the nose, sinuses, and trachea (windpipe) often referred to as rhinitis, sinusitis, tracheitis, or tracheobronchitis. If left untreated, they may progress to lower airway disease involving the bronchi and alveoli, often referred to as bronchitis and pneumonia. Any of these conditions interfere with your pet's ability to breathe and take in appropriate oxygen. Some, especially pneumonia, can result in death.

One very important and often overlooked cause of rhinitis and sinusitis is dental disease. The roots of the teeth in the upper arcade extend into the maxillary sinuses. When plaque and tartar build up, causing gingivitis and periodontal disease, the bacteria involved can enter the sinuses and the bloodstream, resulting in sinusitis and tooth root abscesses. These bacteria may also spread to the lower airways or be disseminated throughout the body via the bloodstream, causing systemic disease as in heart or kidney issues (e.g. endocarditis or pyelonephritis).

Inflammatory/Asthma/Allergy

Noninfectious stimuli or allergens can cause inflammation and/or constriction of the airways resulting in rhinitis, sinusitis, tracheobronchitis, and bronchitis. Most of these conditions must be treated with steroids or antihistamines. Some may require hospitalization, nebulization, and/or oxygen therapy.

Heart And Lung Disease

The heart and lungs work closely together to provide your pet's body with oxygen. Disorders affecting one organ will ultimately affect the other. Heart disease often results in fluid accumulation either inside the alveoli of the lungs (pulmonary edema) or outside the lungs (pleural effusion). This buildup of fluid prevents the lungs from functioning properly and can only be diagnosed and appropriately treated by your veterinarian.

Parasites/Obstruction/Foreign Body

Certain parasites live in the heart and lungs such as heartworms and lung worms. Both cause inflammation and obstruction of the airways and blood vessels, thus interfering with oxygen exchange. Lung worms may be diagnosed with a fecal exam while heartworms are diagnosed with a blood test. Treating these worms can be as serious as the presence of the worms themselves because, when the worms die, the pet's body has to break them down and dispose of them, causing "chunks" of worm to be released into the blood vessels or airways, which may cause thromboembolism or tissue embolism resulting in additional complications. Heartworm disease, carried by a mosquito, can be prevented by having an annual heartworm test performed on your pet and putting him/her on a heartworm preventive medication.

In addition, your pet may inhale different objects that can cause obstructions. Anything your dog will chew, can be inhaled, such as plant awns, sticks, balls, bones, rawhides, treats, etc. There is a type of a fly larva referred to as a "warble" that can be inhaled into the trachea, causing irritation and obstruction. Most of these objects must be surgically removed.

Cancer

Dogs can get primary cancers of the heart or lungs or they can get cancers of the heart or lungs through metastases. For example, hemangiosarcomas of the liver or spleen can spread to the heart, and many types of sarcomas and carcinomas can spread or metastasize to the lungs. Cancer causes consolidation of tissue resulting in obstructions that inhibit the ability of the heart and lungs to function properly.

Anemia

Red blood cells (RBC's) carry oxygen to all of the body's other cells, tissues, and organs. Without oxygen, those other cells, tissues, and organs will die. When there is any disease resulting in blood loss or a decrease in RBCs, the body's cells interpret this loss of oxygen as a respiratory issue. Increased or labored breathing may be observed as the body is trying to take in more oxygen, when the actual problem is that there are not enough RBCs to circulate it.

Seriously folks, if your pet can't breathe, "Yes, should take your dog to the vet!"

All of the above conditions are serious and require veterinary attention for accurate diagnosis and appropriate treatment before they develop into medical emergencies. Open-mouthed breathing or pale, gray, blue, or purple gums are medical emergencies. Without prompt treatment death may quickly result.

Lameness/Joint Swelling/Difficulty Walking

What It Could Be:

1. Injury/Soft Tissue Sprain Or Strain
2. Degenerative Joint Disease (DJD)/Arthritis
3. Congenital/Developmental Bone Or Joint Problem/Growing Pains (e.g. Osteochondritis Dissecans/Panosteitis)
4. Fracture
5. Neurologic (e.g.). Intervertebral Disc Disease, Vertigo, Seizures, Tremors)
6. Dislocated Joint
7. Osteomyelitis - Infection Of The Bone
8. Other Infections (e.g. Lyme Disease)
9. Fever/Vaccination Reactions
10. Cancer
11. Other - Anything Not Mentioned

If your pet is limping and is weight bearing you might try exercise restriction and aspirin therapy for a day or two. Call your veterinarian for the proper dosage and, please keep in mind, that aspirin has the potential to cause a stomach upset and/or GI bleeding in pets, just as it does in people.

Do *not* give your pet Tylenol/acetaminophen or Advil/ibuprofen as these medications are toxic to dogs and especially to cats.

If your pet has not improved within a day or two, "Yes, you should take your dog to the vet!" A thorough physical examination and possibly radiographs (X-Rays) may need to be performed for an accurate diagnosis and treatment.

Many times when your dog has difficulty walking, it is not due to a musculoskeletal problem, but a neurologic problem. If your dog walks into things, is off balance, ataxic (wobbly), is walking in circles, has a head tilt, is reluctant to go up or down stairs or jump up or down off of the furniture or bed, they may actually be exhibiting neurologic symptoms. These symptoms may be caused by vision or hearing loss, vertigo, intervertebral disc disease, thromboembolism or ischemia (e,g. like a stroke where there is a blood clot or another lesion restricting oxygen from a certain area of the brain or spinal cord). Old dogs may have geriatric vestibular disease or age-related neurologic degeneration of the rear limbs. They may also exhibit weakness and tremors.

If your pet is non-weight bearing, "Yes, you should take your dog to the vet!" The incidence of a fracture is much more likely if the pet is not bearing weight or toe-touching at all.

Sometimes, dogs recently vaccinated will present with lameness due to a fever associated with the administration of a vaccination.

In any case, your veterinarian is the only one qualified to evaluate your pet, make a proper diagnosis, and administer appropriate treatment whether medical or surgical.

A Special Note On Lyme Disease

Lyme disease, spread by the deer tick, is endemic in the Northeastern United States. I am not sure if we, as veterinarians, are aware of all of the possible disease manifestations of Lyme disease. I do know that more and more conditions in humans are being attributed to it.

Most pets with Lyme disease present with lameness, fevers, lethargy, inappetence, etc., which may mimic many other disease syndromes. However, in dogs, Lyme disease has been shown to cause an extremely severe and irreversible form of kidney damage. Most of the dogs that get the kidney form of Lyme disease (Lyme nephritis) get sick very quickly and die of kidney failure.

It is extremely important that all dogs in endemic regions be screened for Lyme disease through a blood test and treated if positive. Most dogs that test positive are not sick. They show no clinical signs of illness. However, a positive test result shows that they have been exposed to Lyme disease through a tick bite, even in toy breeds that are infrequently outside. It is strongly recommended that all dogs in endemic areas be treated with appropriate flea and tick medications to avoid exposure to ticks. In addition, all dogs at risk of exposure should be tested and vaccinated for this potentially fatal disease.

8

Seizures

What It Could Be:

1. Epilepsy - Congenital, Acquired, Idiopathic
2. Head Trauma
3. Infection - Meningitis/Myelitis
4. Electrolyte/Metabolic Disorder
5. Thromboembolic/Ischemic Episode
6. Neoplasia
7. Other - Anything Not Mentioned

If your pet is having seizures, "Yes, you need to take your dog to the vet!" The treatment will vary depending on what is causing the seizure. Head trauma needs to be addressed immediately to try to prevent permanent injury to the brain. Any infection will need to be diagnosed and treated with appropriate antimicrobials. Dogs that have recently had puppies may have seizures due to low blood calcium levels as they draw calcium from their blood to produce milk. Puppies and small dogs who are not eating frequently enough may have low blood sugar (glucose) levels. Insulinomas, tumors on the pancreas, may also result in low blood sugar due to excessive insulin secretion.

Seizures may be caused by blood clots or insults resulting in oxygen deprivation to certain areas of the brain.

If no definitive cause for the seizures can be found, or if the diagnosis is epilepsy, your pet may be treated with one or a combination of anticonvulsant medications to decrease the frequency and minimize the severity of the seizures. There is a variety of anticonvulsant drugs available. Your veterinarian is the only one qualified to identify the cause of the seizures and prescribe the appropriate treatment.

9

Porcupine Quills

Unless your dog has only two or three quills, which are readily seen and easy for you to extract, **"Yes, you should take your dog to the vet!"**

Porcupine quills have a barbed tip on them, like the barb at the tip of a fish hook. When pulling them out yourself, you will be ripping this barb backward through your dog's skin. It is extremely painful. Ideally, your dog should be anesthetized by your veterinarian so that a thorough examination of the mouth can be performed. Quills can become lodged between teeth, under the tongue, and in the back of the mouth and throat. If they are left there and swallowed, the sharp point can migrate through the walls of the intestines and cause a fatal septic peritonitis.

Smaller quills or quills that have been broken off can become lodged under the skin and near the eyes. Even with anesthesia and painstaking care, your veterinarian may not be able to find and extract every single quill. In the best-case scenario, any missed quills will fester and will be removed later. Sometimes multiple anesthetic procedures are necessary for deeply embedded quills that migrate and cause problems later.

10

Cuts, Lacerations, and Puncture Wounds

Cuts and lacerations of the head/tongue/mouth or legs/feet may result in profuse bleeding. Please be aware that all cuts, lacerations, and puncture wounds have the potential to become infected. Please also be aware that hair and foreign objects can be caught and stuck up inside what appears to be a small hole or a scratch and will cause infection if not removed (remember porcupine quills?). Many of these lesions are no more than scratches. However, some of these lesions are much more serious than they appear and require surgical exploration.

Puncture wounds and bites into and around the abdomen can be very serious because, if they penetrate the abdominal wall, they can cause an acute peritonitis and death. If they penetrate the rib muscles and create an opening into the chest cavity, they can cause difficulty breathing and death. Severed tendons may underlie a deep skin laceration of the legs and/or feet. Therefore, just because a wound may look minor, doesn't always mean that it is.

If you have a question as to the seriousness of a cut, laceration, or puncture wound, **"Yes, you should take your dog to the vet!"**

11

Toxins/Poisons

Yes, You Should Take Your Dog To The Vet!

With the ingestion of, or exposure to, any toxic substance, you need to contact your veterinarian immediately. Sometimes vomiting needs to be induced and sometimes the induction of vomiting is contraindicated. Sometimes activated charcoal needs to be administered via a stomach tube to prevent or minimize further absorption of the toxin by the gastrointestinal tract. In either of these cases, the actions must be performed immediately, within thirty minutes to an hour of ingestion in order to be effective.

Sometimes the pet needs to be hospitalized for supportive care such as IV fluids. Sometimes there are specific antidotes that must be administered within a short and specific period of time from ingestion. If you wait too long to contact your veterinarian, you may miss the window for administration of the antidote, and it will no longer be effective.

A list of common toxins and poisonous plants is included. In addition, you can call the Animal Poison Control Center at 1-888-426-4435.

Common Toxins:

1. Any human medication. Tylenol/acetaminophen and Advil/ibuprofen and other NSAIDS (nonsteroidal antiinflammatory drugs) in particular.
2. Insecticides - including OTC flea and tick medications
3. Rat poison
4. Antifreeze
5. Chocolate - dark chocolate or baker's chocolate is more toxic
6. Poisonous plants and mushrooms
7. Raisins and grapes
8. Bufo frogs, scorpions, and venomous snakes (depending on the area of the country in which you live).
9. Other - Anything Not Mentioned

A special note on rat poison and antifreeze. **This is so important and so often misunderstood.**

. . .

When a pet ingests rat poison they do *not* get sick immediately. Rat poison ties up Vitamin K-dependent clotting factors and the pet will bleed to death about a week later. With the newer rodenticides, only a tiny amount needs to be eaten to cause death and the effects last for four to six weeks. If you even suspect that your pet may have eaten any amount of rat poison, no matter how small, you need to contact your veterinarian immediately so that they can induce vomiting, administer activated charcoal, and start your pet on supplemental doses of Vitamin K until the effects of the rodenticide wear off.

Only a lap or two of antifreeze needs to be ingested to throw your pet into kidney failure. As with rat poison, your pet may not act sick for a couple of days. However, by then, the damage may be irreversible. If you even think that your pet may have licked antifreeze, you need to get him/her to a veterinarian to start treatment, administer the antidote, and, hopefully, prevent or minimize the damage to the kidneys and/or the possibility of death.

Insecticides used to treat the environment for pests are often toxic to animals. As mentioned previously, watch the ingredients in any over-the-counter flea and tick preparations. Many of these preparations, NOT recommended by your veterinarian, contain insecticides which may be toxic, especially to small dogs and cats.

TOXIC PLANTS

Amaryllis

Anemone

Apple
(seeds)

Apricot
(seeds)

Autumn crocus

Avocado

Azaleas

Baneberry

Belladona

Bird of Paradise

Black Locust

Bleeding Hearts

Bluebonnets

Bottlebrush

Boxwoods

Buckeye
(Horse Chestnuts)

Bushman's Poison

Buttercup

Caladiums

Calla Lily

Carolina Jasmine

Castor Bean

Cherries
(seeds and leaves)

Chinaberry Tree

Coral Plant

Crocus

Crown of Thorns

Daffodils

Daphnes

Death Camas

Delphiniums

Dogwood

Dumbcanes
(Dieffenbachia)

Elderberries

Elephant's Ear

English Laurel

False Hellebores

Fava Bean
(Horse Bean, English Bean or Windsor Bean)

Four-O' Clock

Foxglove

Glory Lily

Hemp
(Marijuana or Hashish)

Hollies

Horse Chestnuts

Hyacinths

Hydrangea

Impatiens

Iris

Ivy

Jasmine, yellow

Jerusalem Cherry

Jimson Weed
(Jamestown Weed, Thornapple, Apple of Peru or Tolquacha)

Lady Slipper
(Moccasin Flower)

Laurels

Lantana

Larkspur

Lily of the Valley

Lobelia

Locoweed

Lupine

Mescal Bean

Milk Bush

Milkweed

Mistletoe

Mock Orange

Monkshood

Morning Glories

Mountain Laurel

Narcissus

Naked Lady

Night-blooming Jasmine

Nutmeg

Oaks
(acorn)

Oleander

Opium Poppy

Peaches
(pits and leaves)

Pear
(seeds)

Peony

Peyote

Philodendrons

Plums
(seeds and leaves)

Poinsettia

Poison Hemlock

Pokeweed
(Pokeberry, Inkberry or Pigeonberry)

Potato
(shoots, berries and sungreen tubers)

Privets

Rattlebox

Rhododendrons

Rhubarb
(leaf blades)

Rosary Pea
(Jequirity Pea, Precor Bean, Prayer Bean or Love Bean)

Skyflowers

Sweet Pea

Tobaccos

Virginian Creeper

Water Hemlock

Wisterias

Yellow Oleander

Yews

26 HOUSEHOLD ITEMS
— POISONOUS TO CATS & DOGS —

Acetaminophen

Batteries

Chocolate

Detergents and fabric softener sheets

Ethylene glycol

Fertilizers

Grapes, raisins, currants, and grape juice

Household cleaners

Insecticides in flea and tick products

Jimson Weed

Kerosene, gasoline, and tiki torch fluids

Lilies - Easter, day, tiger, Japanese and Asiatic varieties

Mothballs

Nonprescription medications

Onions, garlic, leeks, and chives

Prescription medications

Queensland nuts

Rodenticides

Sagi palms

Tobacco

Unbaked bread dough

Veterinary prescriptions

Windshield wiper fluid

Xylitol

Yard products

Zinc toxicity

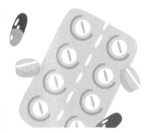

12

He/She Just Ain't Right, Doc

Yes, You Should Take Your Dog To The Vet!

. . .

In another common scenario, a pet owner realizes that the pet is sick or not acting normally but can't really pinpoint what is wrong. Common complaints are that the pet is lethargic, not as active as normal, not eating or drinking normally, won't go up or down the stairs, or is just acting "off."

What It Could Be:

1. Fever/Infection - e.g. Ear Or Tooth
2. Nausea/Upset Stomach
3. Pain - e.g. Back Pain, Abdominal Pain
4. Systemic Disease - e.g. Heart, Liver, Kidney, Pancreas
5. Cancer
6. Anemia
7. Other - Anything Not Mentioned or Mentioned Previously

Because our pets cannot speak to us, we have to try to figure out what is wrong by observing their behaviors. While most owners are very good at this, some dogs do not read the book—so there are some things that are not obvious. For example, unless you take your pet's temperature with a rectal thermometer, you may not know if they are running a fever. Normal body temperature for a dog or cat is around 100–102 degrees Fahrenheit. Your pet may or may not feel warm to you (and a warm, dry nose does not indicate whether your pet has a fever). Usually, pets will feel warmer in the non-haired or thin-haired areas of their body, like their ears or abdomen. Many times dogs with a fever will feel lethargic and experience inappetence.

Your pet may also feel nauseous but is not actively vomiting. You know, that feeling of trying not to puke? Again, your pet may feel lethargic, they may be experiencing inappetence, and they may feel nauseous, but, because they are not actively showing any signs, all you see is that they don't want to eat and don't feel good.

Reluctance to climb stairs or jump up on or down from furniture may indicate pain, such as back pain (intervertebral disc disease) or arthritis.

If your pet is anemic, they have a low-red-blood-cell count; their cells are not receiving enough oxygen. They may act tired, their gums will be pale, they will be lethargic, and they may not want to eat. There are numerous causes of anemia including: blood loss, cancer, anemia of chronic disease, and immune-mediated disorders (Autoimmune Hemolytic Anemia - AIHA or Immune-mediated Thrombocytopenia - IMT) in which the immune system itself attacks its own red blood cells or platelets.

Depending on the area of the country in which you live, there are various blood parasites or bacteria causing such diseases as Babesiosis, Hemobartonellosis, Rocky Mountain Spotted Fever, Ehrlichiosis, or Anaplasmosis. I will not go into a detailed explanation of each of these disease syndromes because this list is not all inclusive, varies with your pet and the area of the country in which you live, and all require your veterinarian to diagnose and treat appropriately.

People with new puppies and kittens need to monitor their behavior, appetite, and the color of their gums. Many parasitic infestations will cause anemia. Again this list is not all inclusive, but parasites that can cause anemia include roundworms, hookworms, whipworms, and fleas. An infestation of these parasites may require a blood transfusion to avoid death. With early detection and proper veterinary intervention most of these cases are generally treatable and have good outcomes.

Pets with chronic (long-term) disease such as heart disease, liver disease, kidney disease, and cancer may present with anemia as their bone marrow becomes suppressed and cannot produce the red blood cells their body needs to support their demand for oxygen and glucose.

Your veterinarian is the only person qualified to make all of these distinctions. Due to their extensive medical training, many syndromes can be detected or suspected and confirmed through a thorough physical examination followed by necessary diagnostic tests.

13

Anal Sacs - "The Butt-Scootin' Boogie"

What It Could Be:

1. Irritation/Infection Of The Perianal Area, Vulva, Anus
2. Your Pet Trying To Express The Anal Sacs
3. Anal Sac Abscess
4. Anal Sac Tumor
5. Other - Anything Not Mentioned

Both dogs and cats have two scent glands (similar to those of a ferret or a skunk) located near the anus at approximately the five o'clock and seven o'clock positions. Your pet expresses a liquid, creamy- to dark-colored material contained in the anal sacs through ducts leading to the opening of the anus during bowel movements or when the pet becomes scared or startled. This material has a distinct strong "fish-like" odor. (Frankly, it is nasty and stinks bad!) The purpose of this material is to help your pet mark its territory.

If your pet spends an exceptional amount of time licking its perianal area or scoots its bottom across the carpet or the grass, contrary to popular belief, it is *not* because they have worms. They either have an infection or irritation to the perigenital area (e.g. from urine scald, vulvar fold pyoderma, or diarrhea), or they are trying to express their anal sacs. The material in the anal sacs is normally liquid and easy for the pet to express itself, however, sometimes the material becomes very thick or dry and clogs the ducts so that the material may not be normally expressed. If it cannot be expressed, it continues to build up inside the anal sac until it abscesses and ruptures through the skin.

Your veterinarian or veterinary technician will express the anal sacs with a gloved hand and examine it to make sure there is no blood or pus in it. If an anal sac abscess is present, the duct and the anal sac will both be flushed to reestablish a patent opening, and your pet will be treated with antibiotics.

A special note on long-haired breeds of dogs: feces may be stuck to and dried to the hair around your pet's perigenital region, causing obstruction of elimination. Please check your pet's butt and have a "potty path" shaved if necessary.

So, if you see your pet licking excessively or doing the "Butt Scootin' Boogie" across the floor, "Yes, you should take your dog to the vet!"

14

Routine Annual Physical Examinations

Yes, You Should Take Your Dog To The Vet!

. . .

Perhaps I should have made this chapter one. Many people only take their dog to the vet if they receive a vaccination reminder in the mail or if they see that their pet is seriously ill. Although vaccinations are important, the annual physical examination is the most vital part of the appointment. Many medical issues and disease syndromes are discovered during the routine physical examination, even though the pet owner has not noticed that the pet has a problem or we get the "Oh, by the way, Doc, he/she's doing this..." If caught early, the prognosis for a successful and treatable outcome to most disease syndromes is greatly enhanced.

Medical Issues Commonly Discovered By Routine Physical Examination:

1. Eye Problems
2. Skin And Ear Problems
3. Dental Disease/Diseases Of The Mouth
4. Anemia
5. Heart Disease
6. Respiratory Disease
7. Fevers

8. Enlarged Lymph Nodes
9. Abdominal Masses/Tumors
10. Liver And/Or Kidney Disease
11. Bladder Stones/Urinary Tract Disease
12. Cancer
13. Parasites - Fleas, Ticks, Worms, Coccidia, etc.
14. Neurologic Problems
15. Weight Loss Or Gain
16. Reproductive Problems
17. Other - Anything Not Mentioned

All of these issues prompt your veterinarian to try to identify a cause as to why they exist. This list is not meant to be exhaustive, only to demonstrate the importance of a thorough annual physical examination. Depending on your pet's age, medical history, and physical exam findings, other tests may be recommended in order to detect diseases that may not have manifested clinical signs yet. For example, bloodwork may be recommended to identify early stages of liver or kidney disease. Radiographs may be recommended to assess the severity of a heart murmur, a lung issue, or the presence of bladder stones. Early detection of these diseases increases the chances of successful treatment.

So, for a complete and thorough annual physical examination and early detection of potential medical issues, "Yes, you should take your dog to the vet!" Senior pets may need to be examined more often, i.e. every three to six months.

15

Spay/Neuter

Yes, You Should Take Your Dog To The Vet!

. . .

If you have no desire to breed your dog, she/he should be spayed/neutered. Veterinarians have differing opinions as to the best age for spaying or neutering your pet. Certainly, veterinarians working for humane societies and animal shelters support spaying or neutering at an early age, prior to adoption, to prevent more unwanted litters from winding back up at the shelter. However, most veterinarians in private practice agree that some-where around six months of age is appropriate. At that age, the puppy is old enough to be a better anesthetic candidate, but is not yet old enough to procreate. In addition to preventing unwanted litters of puppies, there are significant health advantages to having your dog spayed or neutered at a young age. Even if you do want to breed your female, there is a significant advantage to breed-ing, then having your female spayed before she is two years old or before her fourth heat.

When a female dog is spayed, the uterus and ovaries are removed (ovariohysterectomy) thus preventing heat cycles and breeding. There is evidence to support that there is a significant reduction in the incidence of mammary gland tumors (breast cancer) in dogs spayed before their fourth heat or before they are two years old. In dogs, 50 percent of mammary gland tumors are malignant. That number approaches 80 percent in cats. Ovarian cancer and pyometras (life-threatening uterine infections) can also be prevented. The older and fatter your pet is, the more difficult the surgery, both from the doctor's and the patient's standpoint. If the female is in heat, or if she is older and overweight, there is significantly more bleeding, and the ligaments become very friable, making them much more difficult to clamp and ligate.

If a female dog has a pyometra, her uterus is full of pus, so she is very sick. The treatment for a pyometra is an emergency ovariohysterectomy. The surgery must be performed to save the patient's life, but now becomes a "high-risk" surgery depending on how sick she is at the time of presentation. The veterinarian is now performing a major abdominal surgery on a sick, old, fat dog instead of a young, healthy dog.

When male dogs are neutered (castrated) the testicles are removed. If done at a young age, not only are inappropriate sexual behaviors, like territorial marking (hiking their leg and peeing all over stuff) and roaming and chasing after female dogs in heat, minimized, but life-threatening conditions such as testicular cancer and prostate disease can be prevented or minimized. Once these disorders manifest, the treatment is to neuter your dog. However, just as in the case of the older female dog, you are now neutering an old, sick dog instead of a young, healthy dog. Thus, the anesthetic and surgical risk is higher. In addition, if the disease process is a malignant neoplasm (cancer), the prognosis is generally poor due to the process itself and the propensity for metastasis or spread to other body organs such as the lungs.

The bottom line is that many of the above disease processes can virtually be avoided, or at least minimized, by having your pet spayed or neutered at a young age.

16

Dentistry

Yes, You Should Take Your Dog To The Vet!

. . .

As humans, what are the recommendations dentists give to us as far as care of our own teeth? We are told to brush and floss at least twice daily and after every meal. Then, it is recommended that we go to the dentist for prophylactic teeth cleaning procedures every six months. Can you imagine *never* brushing or flossing your teeth?

Up to 80 percent of all dogs have some form of dental disease by age four. This disease may be in the form of tartar build up, gingivitis, periodontal disease, or tooth infections/abscesses. In general, small and toy breeds of dogs experience this tartar and plaque build up at a much earlier age than larger breeds of dogs.

Routine annual physical examinations will allow your veterinarian to evaluate your pet's mouth and the need for a dental prophylaxis procedure. This procedure is similar to our six-month dental cleaning. The "dental" is meant to help prevent more significant dental disease in the future by removing accumulated plaque and tartar before it can progress to gingivitis, periodontal disease, or tooth abscesses. In general, a thorough oral examination can only be performed while your pet is under anesthesia. Not only does anesthesia allow for a thorough examination of the mouth, it also allows for dental radiographs, the cleaning, periodontal treatments, and extractions, if needed.

As mentioned previously, the bacteria that accumulate in the mouth, under the plaque and tartar, can enter the bloodstream via the inflamed gingiva (gums) and can seed other important body systems such as the heart (bacterial endocarditis), the respiratory system (sinusitis, bronchitis, pneumonia), the liver (hepatitis), or the kidneys (pyelonephritis), etc.

What can be done at home? Only preventive care can be performed at home. Owners should brush their pet's teeth on a regular basis. There are many brands of dental kits, toothbrushes, finger brushes, and toothpaste on the market today. There are also numerous tartar control diets, treats, and toys. However, once disease sets in, your veterinarian is the only one qualified to diagnose and treat the condition. So, if you notice that your pet has "bad breath," bleeding from the mouth, a broken or loose tooth, swelling over the cheeks between the mouth and the eyes, or pain while chewing, "Yes, you should take your dog to the vet!"

Conclusion

In conclusion, please consider your veterinarian as a friend and a valuable resource to help you provide the best care for your pet. Most small animal practitioners can be compared to human pediatricians. Your dog or cat is not "just a dog or cat" to us. Most people now consider their pets as beloved family members and even "children." Veterinarians have undergone extensive training in diagnosing disease syndromes in animals that cannot speak to us through language. They cannot verbalize to us what is wrong or how they are feeling. We study, not only medicine, but behavior in multiple animal species to be able diagnose and treat them appropriately. As veterinarians, we do have your pets' best interests at heart! With that in mind, if you have any questions regarding your pet's health, "Yes, you should take your dog to the vet!"

Acknowledgments

I would like to acknowledge my family, my friends, and all of my clients who have supported me and my veterinary practice for the past thirty years. Thank you for listening to me talk about writing this book for years and for reading the rough drafts, offering your honest opinions, and helping me to make this book a reality.

About the Author

Dr. Renee Fisher graduated as valedictorian of Athens Area High School in Athens, PA in 1976. She received her BS in Animal Behavior from Bucknell University in 1980 and her DVM degree from the University of Florida's College of Veterinary Medicine in 1986. Dr. Fisher has owned and operated the Milan Veterinary Clinic since 1991 and, since then, has supported the Bradford County Humane Society in Ulster, PA and Stray Haven Humane Society in Waverly, NY.

.

Made in the USA
Monee, IL
23 June 2023

36883091R00066